The Hit Singles
Atomic Kitten

Exclusive distributors:
Music Sales Limited, 8/9 Frith Street, London W1D 3JB, England.
Music Sales Pty Limited, 120 Rothschild Avenue, Rosebery, NSW 2018, Australia.

Order No. AM976844
ISBN 0-7119-9876-0
This book © Copyright 2003 by Wise Publications.

Compiled by Lucy Holliday.
Photographs courtesy of London Features International.
Printed in the United Kingdom by Caligraving Limited, Thetford, Norfolk.

Your Guarantee of Quality:
As publishers, we strive to produce every book to the highest commercial standards.
This book has been carefully designed to minimise awkward page turns and to make playing from it a real pleasure.
Particular care has been given to specifying acid-free, neutral-sized paper made from pulps which have not been elemental chlorine bleached.
This pulp is from farmed sustainable forests and was produced with special regard for the environment.
Throughout, the printing and binding have been planned to ensure a sturdy, attractive publication which should give years of enjoyment.
If your copy fails to meet our high standards, please inform us and we will gladly replace it.

www.musicsales.com

Wise Publications
London / New York / Paris / Sydney / Copenhagen / Berlin / Madrid / Tokyo

Eternal Flame

Words & Music by Billy Steinberg, Tom Kelly & Susanna Hoffs

-ing? Do you un-der-stand?__ Do you feel the same__ or am I on-ly

dream — ing? Is this burn-ing an e — ter-nal flame?

2. I be-lieve__ it's meant to__ be__ dar-ling,__ I watch you when__ you are sleep-

-ing, you be-long with me.__ Do you feel the same__ or am I on-ly

Repeat ad lib. to fade

6

The Last Goodbye

Words & Music by Tor Erik Hermansen, Hallgeir Rustan, Mikkel Eriksen,
Danny Poku, Espen Lind & Amund Bjorklund

'cause we could - n't seem to find a way__ for love__ to stay.

If you had a - no - ther night to give__ I would have a - no - ther night to live.

Fine

But you're nev - er gon - na see me cry the last_____ good - bye.

Verse 2:
Is it cloudy where you are tonight?
Are the neon lights shining bright?
Are you looking for a place to stay to get away?
And the days are horses down the hill
Running fast with no time to kill
And the truth is that we'll never know where love will flow
Aim high, shoot low
(You gotta aim high and shoot low baby).

Ain't no headlights on the road tonight *etc.*

It's OK!

Words & Music by Tor Erik Hermansen, Hallgeir Rustan & Mikkel Eriksen

Verse 2:
Well now you've got to where you wanted
Like I knew you would
Cash, car, house, it's all good.
It's the why you never came around here no more
Like you did before
Got it all, that's the way it seems
Looks like you live your dream
And I hope your love it turns out for the better now
When I'm not around
I believed in you, I must have been a fool
All my dreams were with you.

I say it's O. K. I can promise you *etc.*

The Tide Is High (Get The Feeling)

Words & Music by John Holt, Howard Barrett, Tyrone Evans, Bill Padley & Jem Godfrey

Verse 4:
Every girl wants you to be her man
But I'll wait right here till it's my turn
I'm not the kind of girl who gives up just like that
Oh no.

Whole Again

Words & Music by Stuart Kershaw, Andy McCluskey, Bill Padley & Jeremy Godfrey

cry,___ but you can make me whole___ a - gain.___

2. If you see me with a - no-ther man laugh-ing and___ jok-
(Verse 3 see block lyric)

-ing, do-ing what I can,___ I won't put you down,_ 'cause I want you a-

round,_ and you can make me whole_ a - gain.___

Look-in' back on when we first met, I_____ can-not es-
-cape___ and I can-not for-get._____ Ba - by you're the one, you___ still turn me
on,___ you can make me whole__ a - gain.___
For now I'll have to wait, but ba - by if you change your

25

mind, don't be too late 'cause I just can't go on, it's al-rea-dy been too

long, but you could make me whole a-gain. Ooh, ooh, ooh, ah, ooh, ah.

Look-in' back on when we first met, I_____ can-not es-

-cape_____ and I can-not for-get._____ Ba - by you're the

Verse 2:
Time is laying heavy on my heart
Seems I've got too much of it since we've been apart
My friends make me smile, if only for a while
You can make me whole again.

You Are

Words & Music by Steve Mac, Wayne Hector, Alistair Tennent & Paul Gendler

♩ = 100

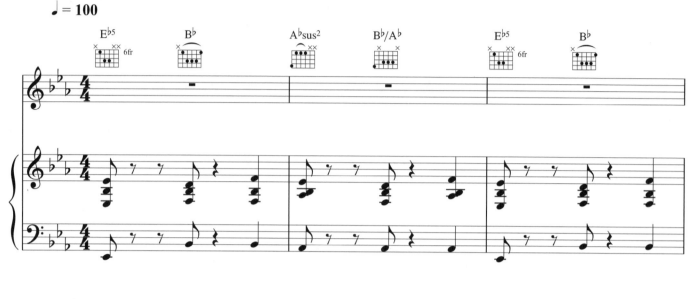

1. May-be you think__ you're not right for me that
(Verse 2: see block lyric)

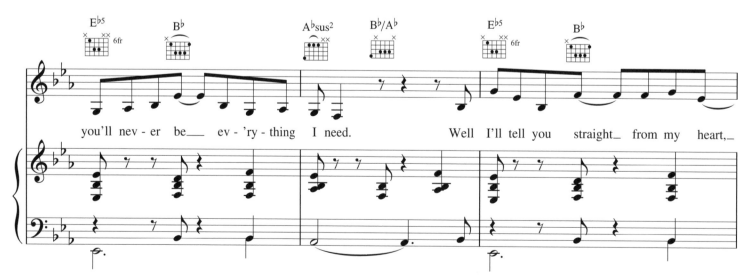

you'll nev-er be__ ev-'ry-thing I need.   Well I'll tell you straight__ from my heart,__

29

30

Verse 2:

If ever I wanted to run away
I'd go only if you would come with me
'Cause no one can talk to my heart
Like you are, you are.

If I did for you what you do for me
And I'm on your mind every time you sleep
Say the words and no matter how far
I'll be where you are.

You are, you are *etc.*